My Emotions and Me

MY EMOTIONS AND ME

An Hachette UK Company
www.hachette.co.uk

Vie Books, an imprint of Summersdale Publishers Ltd
Part of Octopus Publishing Group Limited
Carmelite House
50 Victoria Embankment
LONDON
EC4Y 0DZ
UK

www.summersdale.com

Printed and bound in China

ISBN: 978-1-80007-994-6

WEST NORTHAMPTONSHIRE COUNCIL	
60000534890	
Askews & Holts	
CC	

Substantial discounts on bulk quantities of Summersdale books are available to corporations, professional associations and other organizations. For details contact general enquiries: telephone: +44 (0) 1243 771107 or email: enquiries@summersdale.com.

My Emotions and Me

A Graphic Novel to Help You Understand Your Feelings

Art-mella

Why this comic book?

I DON'T KNOW ABOUT YOU, BUT I'VE STRUGGLED WITH MY EMOTIONS...

BACK AND FORTH BETWEEN PERIODS OF EMOTIONAL DROUGHT...

... AND MEGA STORMS

I COULDN'T GO ON LIKE THAT ANYMORE, SO I DECIDED TO START AN INVESTIGATION!

Let's see if we can find the need that's hiding the emotion.

NVC
(Nonviolent Communication)
training course

I'm going to teach you how to cancel a thought that's making you suffer.

Whoa! We can do that??

(Quantum Healing workshop)

I LEARNED SO, SO MANY AMAZING TECHNIQUES AND IT MADE ME WONDER:

Why aren't we taught at school how our emotions work??

I'm sure it'd be at least as useful as learning math!

RIGHT, THEN! I'M GONNA WRITE A COMIC BOOK ABOUT EMOTIONS!!

My Emotions and Me

THANK YOU TO ALL YOU READERS FOR YOUR TRUST, SUPPORT AND ENCOURAGEMENT. TO OLIVIER FOR HIS LOVE, INSPIRATION, READING AND SHARING. TO MY PUBLISHERS ALINE AND ALBERT DE PÉTIGNY FOR THEIR TRUST IN ME, AND FOR THEIR SPARKLING PERSONALITIES. TO MY FAMILY FOR ALWAYS BEING THERE. TO ALL THE PEOPLE WHO INSPIRED ME TO CREATE THIS COMIC BOOK THROUGH THEIR TEACHINGS, IN WORKSHOPS, CONFERENCES OR JUST IN LIFE.

The socks plead not guilty

I can't take it anymore! Foxy left his socks lying on the couch AGAIN!

IT'S DRIVING ME CRAZY!

You ARE angry, aren't you!

YOU BET I AM!

THIS CAN'T GO ON! HIS IRRESPONSIBLE BEHAVIOUR HAS TO STOP!

What if I were to tell you that the cause of your anger is not Foxy or his socks?

Not so fast, my dear Watson. Let's take a closer look!

Can you think of anyone who has a different reaction to the sight of Foxy's socks?

Um... sure. Porky, my other flatmate. It makes him laugh. But he's a pig!

And my friend Rattine just whistles as she picks them up... But she's way too nice!

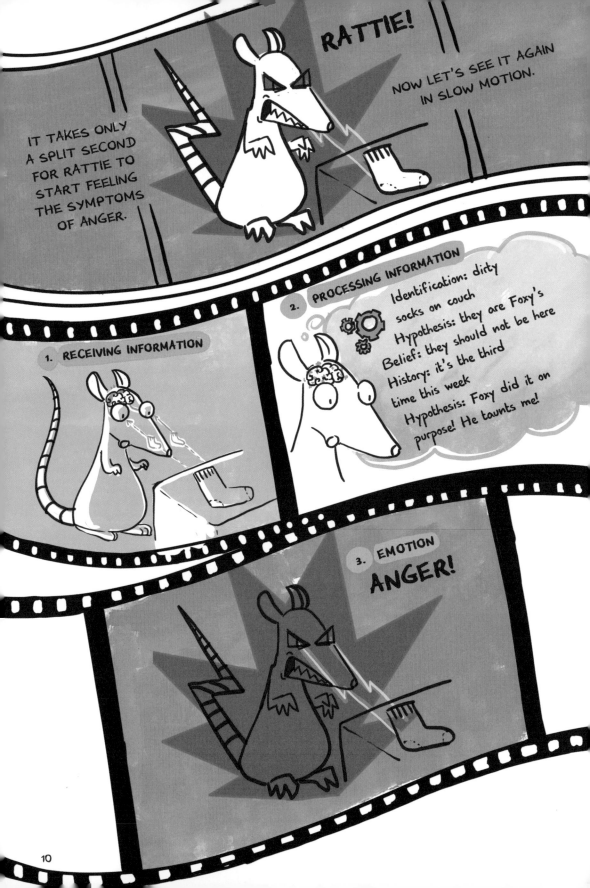

You see, like Lulumineuse* says, "Emotions are the result of how you process the initial information."

THE PROOF IS THAT OTHERS REACT DIFFERENTLY TO THE SAME INFORMATION:

Are you telling me that what's to blame is not the information...

But... How I process the information? So... it's ME???

Yup! We're each responsible for our own emotions! Good news, right?

*Lulumineuse inspires thousands of people to connect with their own inner power.

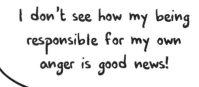

I don't see how my being responsible for my own anger is good news!

Well, if what's bothering you only depends on you, then feeling better depends on you too!

Oh, right! I'd never thought about it like that before.

Remember, in some situations anger is justified, because it can signal to you when something is wrong and help to keep you safe. However, when you have a strong emotional reaction to something relatively harmless, you can try thinking about how you are responsible for your own emotions.

Activity 1
Listen to your thoughts

What are you thinking about right now? Sit quietly and pay attention to your thoughts. Write or doodle the words and pictures that come to your mind in the stars on this page.

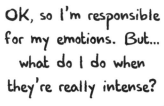

Welcoming an emotion

OK, so I'm responsible for my emotions. But... what do I do when they're really intense?

It's simple: you welcome them.

Welcome them??

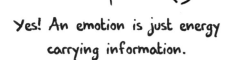

Yes! An emotion is just energy carrying information.

I've got some important news!

THE ONLY THING IT CARES ABOUT IS THAT YOU RECEIVE THE MESSAGE.

IF YOU SHUT THE DOOR ON IT, IT'LL JUST KNOCK HARDER TO MAKE YOU HEAR!

IT WILL KEEP KNOCKING, HARDER AND HARDER, UNTIL YOU RECEIVE THE MESSAGE. IT HAS EVEN BEEN KNOWN TO ASK YOUR BODY TO RELAY THE MESSAGE (WHICH COULD EXPLAIN SOME ILLNESSES).*

*See Michel Odoul, author of *Dis-moi où tu as mal, je te dirai pourquoi* (Tell me where it hurts, I'll tell you why).

BUT IF YOU WELCOME IT IN, IT LEAVES RIGHT AWAY!

IF IT'S BEEN KNOCKING FOR A WHILE, THE DOOR MIGHT GET STUCK, SO THE EMOTION MAY REQUIRE SOME EXTRA LOVE AND ATTENTION.

Oh! How do I do that?

You can simply tap your karate chop point.* That helps open the door.

At the same time, you say:

"Even though I feel... (anger, for example)... I deeply and completely love and accept myself." (three times!)

OK!

TAP TAP!

Even though I feel anger, I deeply and completely love and accept myself. (three times!)

TAP! TAP

Mmm... Feels better already!

YES! THE EMOTION CALMS DOWN WHEN IT KNOWS IT IS ACCEPTED AND WILL BE WELCOMED. (See page 26 for more detail!)

*An acupuncture point that helps clear conflicts of the subconscious, negative thoughts and more.

Now, close your eyes.
Turn your attention inward.
Tell me three things that are
happening in your body right now.

Um... I'm tense.

How can you tell? Where in
your body do you feel tense?

In my eyebrows.
I'm frowning.

OK. What else?

My shoulder
muscles are tense.

Um...

Good. What else?

What do you feel? Pushing? Pulling? Does it sting? Is it cold? Hot? Is it going up? Going down?

Going up.
It's in my belly.

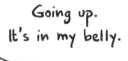

Great. Let it do what it has to.

I don't like this.

What if just this once you let the tension rise?
See what happens.

OK...

It's moving!
It's moving into my throat!

Very good, let it keep going.

My breath is short.

Great! Let it be short, and just observe.

?

It's gone??

That means it's over!

Well done! You've welcomed your emotion fully!

Totally! You can even use it for really big emotions like phobias, anger tantrums, compulsive eating, jealousy, painful shyness, anxiety, etc.

Incredible! And I don't even have to use any words??

SPITE

BITTERNESS

WHEN YOU'RE EXPERIENCING AN EMOTION, IT'S MUCH EASIER TO FEEL THE EMOTION RATHER THAN PUT IT INTO WORDS.

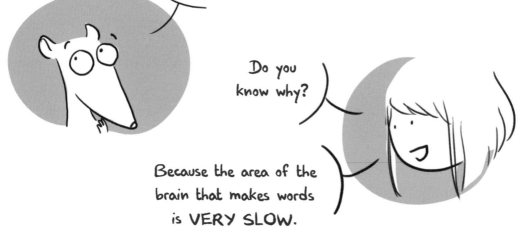

True. For me it's difficult to find my words right away.

Do you know why?

Because the area of the brain that makes words is VERY SLOW.

WHOA! WHAT WAS THAT??

EMOTIONS

WORDS

TOO SLOW!

IF WE TAKE A LOOK AT THE THREE BRAINS WE'VE GOT IN OUR HEADS*, THERE'S:

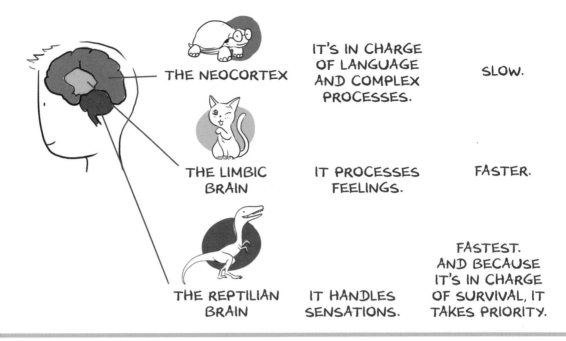

THE NEOCORTEX	IT'S IN CHARGE OF LANGUAGE AND COMPLEX PROCESSES.	SLOW.
THE LIMBIC BRAIN	IT PROCESSES FEELINGS.	FASTER.
THE REPTILIAN BRAIN	IT HANDLES SENSATIONS.	FASTEST. AND BECAUSE IT'S IN CHARGE OF SURVIVAL, IT TAKES PRIORITY.

SO, THE QUICK WAY TO WELCOME YOUR EMOTIONS IS TO FOCUS ON YOUR SENSATIONS. (REPTILIAN BRAIN = MAXIMUM SPEED!)

OF COURSE, IF YOU HAVE THE TIME, YOU CAN ALSO WELCOME YOUR EMOTIONS WITH WORDS.

WE'LL TALK ABOUT HOW TO DO THIS A BIT LATER.

Inspired by Luc Geiger's NERTI technique [Rapid Emotional Clearing of Subconscious Traumas] - similar to the TIPI method.

*This is a simplification, of course, because our brains are far more complex!

Activity 2
Welcoming an emotion

Some emotions can feel uncomfortable like anger or worry, but there are things you can do to help you cope with them. One of them is the karate chop exercise that Rattie and Art-mella try together on p19.

Here's what to do:

1. Identify a situation that made you feel uncomfortable emotions, such as anger or worry. For example: when my friend took my ball from my hands.

2. Try to remember the details of the situation and let your emotions rise again. Measure the intensity of your emotions before you do the exercise on the calm-o-meter below.

3. Now, try the karate chop exercise.

At the same time you say, for example: "Even if I felt shocked when they took the ball off my hands, and I don't understand, I deeply and completely love myself."

4. You can do several rounds and let the thoughts and emotions evolve.

* **Round 2:** Even if I want to cry, I deeply and completely love myself.

* **Round 3:** Even if I feel anger, I deeply and completely love myself.

* **Round 4:** Hm... I understand they wanted to play with the ball and were very excited. I sometimes feel excited too. It was awkward but I know they didn't intend to hurt my feelings.

5. Measure the intensity of your emotions after doing the exercise on the calm-o-meter below.

Mindfulness means giving your full attention to something, taking your time and paying attention to the present moment. Practising mindfulness can have many positive effects on how you feel. Here's a list of its magical benefits:

It makes you feel more relaxed

It can help you worry less

It increases your attention span

It helps you slow down and make fewer mistakes

It improves your listening and learning because it increases your attention span

It helps you to cope with difficult feelings

Get in touch with how you're feeling like Rattie and try this calming mindfulness exercise. Check your emotions on the calm-o-meter scale before you begin.

* Find a comfy place to sit or lie down.

* Close your eyes.

* Slowly scan your body from the top of your head to the tips of your toes.

* Where in your body do you feel tense?

* Do you feel warm or cold, or just right?

* What other feelings are you experiencing in your body?

* Can you feel a pushing or pulling?

* Pay attention to the feelings evolving and transforming, and just observe them.

* Is the first feeling you noticed still there?

* What about the second and third feeling?

* What's happening now?

* How's your breathing?

* If your body wants to move, stretch, change position and let it do so. Your body knows what it needs to find its balance.

* Let what's happening evolve, and just give it your attention.

Now, open your eyes and check that calm-o-meter again!

What direction are you headed?

"Emotion" comes from the latin "emovere" which means "to move".

Emotions are motion!

Basically, an emotion is energy that puts us into motion.

So it might be interesting to know what direction the energy is taking us.

Mh?

Believe it or not, our four basic emotions each have a specific direction and function!*

Really?

Yes!

Pushing away

For example, ANGER IS A MOVEMENT THAT PUSHES AWAY. It's useful for setting limits and protecting your personal space.

Aha! That's why I'm angry with Foxy!

Ha ha... Sure, that's part of it!

I'm defending my personal space against his filthy socks!

PLEASURE - JOY

Moving forward

PLEASURE/JOY IS WHAT ALLOWS YOU TO MOVE FORWARD.

IT'S USEFUL FOR HELPING YOU MOVE TOWARDS YOUR GOALS.

Of course! Makes sense: no pleasure, no motivation!

*Inspired by a web conference led by Adrien Piret.

SADNESS

Letting go

SADNESS IS A DOWNWARD MOVEMENT.

IT'S USEFUL FOR HELPING YOU TO LET GO OF YOUR ATTACHMENTS (TO A LOVED ONE, A PROJECT, ILLUSIONS), AND TO FREE YOU FROM THEM.

Yes! Now that I know that, I appreciate crying a lot more!

Oh!
It's true that sometimes after crying I feel better! So being sad actually has a purpose??

FEAR

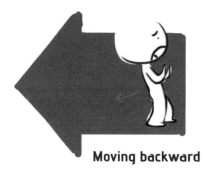

Moving backward

AND FEAR IS A BACKWARD MOVEMENT.

IT'S USEFUL IF YOU HAVE TO REACT QUICKLY IN THE EVENT OF PHYSICAL DANGER, OR TO BECOME AWARE OF YOUR PSYCHOLOGICAL BOUNDARIES.

Hm...

So, if pleasure helps us move forward, and fear makes us go backward...

... then if we want to move forward, it's totally counterproductive to worry about it??

You got it!

Can you believe I figured this out only a few months ago?!

WORRYING ABOUT NOT ADVANCING IS LIKE ACCELERATING WITH THE HANDBRAKE ON!

WHY AM I NOT MOVING FORWARD??

FEAR FEAR FEAR FEAR FEAR FEAR

YAY!!! IT'S SO MUCH BETTER WHEN I RELEASE THE FEAR AND STEP ON THE PLEASURE!

Art-mella

IT WEARS YOU OUT... AND YOU DON'T GO VERY FAST!

PLUS, IT GOBBLES UP TONS OF ENERGY!!

Activity 4
All emotions are OK!

It's true! While some of them don't feel very nice when you're feeling them, that doesn't mean that they're bad or wrong, or that they can hurt you.

See if you can answer these questions by circling the emotion.

> You tidy your room for a play date and are really excited to have your friend round, but they leave your room in a terrible mess.
>
> How do you feel?
>
> anger / sadness / fear / pleasure

ANGER

SADNESS

The teacher asks you to answer a difficult question and you're not sure of the answer at first, but then you get it right!

How do you feel?

anger / sadness / fear / pleasure

Your ice cream falls on the floor when you have just bought it with your pocket money.

How do you feel?

anger / sadness / fear / pleasure

FEAR

PLEASURE - JOY

Mind, body and breathing

An emotion is energy travelling through the body.

I can't take it anymore!!!

Argh!

A BIT LIKE ELECTRICITY!

(Emotion: 12 volts)

The first thing to check is whether your body is fit enough to handle the emotions, and if not, you should strengthen it!

I feel totally overwhelmed by what is happening!!!

Hm... It's been two weeks since I've exercised.

Alright, time for some exercise!

State of my body | State of my mind

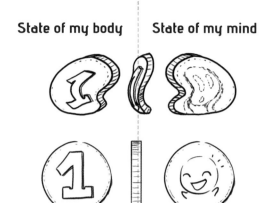

In Eastern philosophies, they say the body and the mind are two sides of the same coin.

And since it's easier to reshape the body than the mind, that's a good place to start!!

So doing exercise, eating well and sleeping well keeps us in shape?

Yes.
And breathing well too!

Really?

Actually, your breathing regulates itself automatically, and with it, your emotions.

This is really getting me all steamed up!

 Pffff!!!

AND TA-DA! THE STEAM IS GONE!!

 Oh yeah! HA HA HA!

YOU LAUGH TO LET THE JOY OUT!

 AAAAH! RAAAAH!

YOU YELL TO LET YOUR FEAR OR ANGER OUT.

 Phew!

AND WE MAKE LOTS OF LITTLE SOUNDS WITHOUT EVEN REALIZING, WHICH HELP US STAY HEALTHY!

But conscious breathing is a whole ART in itself! There are lots of techniques and practices that people spend years studying, like qigong in China or pranayama techniques in India.

Ha ha! Years spent learning how to breathe??

Yes, because it's so effective!

For instance, there's a breathing technique called "Afghan walking" that lets ordinary men, women and children walk for days without getting tired!

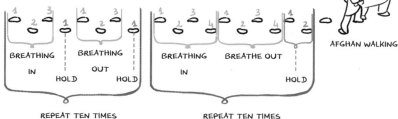

BREATHING IN | HOLD | BREATHING OUT | HOLD

REPEAT TEN TIMES

BREATHING IN | BREATHE OUT | HOLD

REPEAT TEN TIMES

AFGHAN WALKING

Wow!

Because the air you breathe nourishes you.

Conscious breathing actually nourishes and strengthens your body naturally.

Will you teach me some breathing?

Sure! You can start with something fun like a "three-part breath*":
(It's like a wave! I love it!)

INHALE THROUGH YOUR NOSE:

(1) into the belly　　(2) then the chest　(3) and then the collarbone

(One hand on your belly and the other on your chest to help feel the movement.)

EXHALE THROUGH YOUR NOSE:

(1) let the collarbone back down　(2) empty your chest　(3) and then empty your belly

*learned in yoga class.

Mmm... That's so nice...

I love doing it lying down, that way I'm totally relaxed!

But you can do it pretty much any time of day, for just a couple of minutes. Become aware of your breathing and empty out your lungs completely to let go of any tension.

(Breathe through your nose as you inflate your belly.)

Activity 5
Help the tension make its way through the maze and out of the body

An uncomfortable emotion is like a dragon trying to get out of your body! The evolving feelings in your body are like the dragon's footprints while it searches for its way out. Help the dragon find its way out by giving attention to its footprints!

Phew, that's better!

Activity 6
Stand tall

Just making small changes to how you stand or move can give you a big boost and help you feel more confident. Strike a pose — according to scientists, standing tall for two minutes can give you an instant happiness and confidence boost. Try standing tall and see how much better you feel!

stand with your feet apart and your hands in the air, like you've scored the winning goal in the match.

Colour in the happy-o-meter to check your happy rating!

Our emotional compass

Our emotions also work a bit like a COMPASS.

pleasure · joy · anger · sadness · fear

JOY and PLEASURE show us the natural direction for fulfilment and development.

FRUSTRATION

Well, I for one do not always feel joy and pleasure!!

Interesting! What do you think you can do about that?

OFTEN, WHEN WE'RE FRUSTRATED IT MEANS THAT OUR ENERGY IS BEING MISDIRECTED.

ARGH! I'M FRUSTRATED BECAUSE I'M NOT DOING WHAT REALLY MAKES ME HAPPY!

LITTLE PLEASURES HELP US STAY ON TRACK!

Our five imaginary lives

Sometimes our compass stays in the cupboard too long, and it can go a bit off... it's hard to tell what brings us joy anymore or what direction to head in.

HERE'S A FUN GAME TO GET IT WORKING AGAIN. I FOUND IT SUPER HELPFUL, AND SO DID A LOT OF MY FRIENDS:

ALERT!

PLEASE FINISH YOUR LIST
BEFORE YOU KEEP READING!!

Activity 7 - Part 1
Five lives exercise

What five lives would you love to live? Write them down in the thought bubbles below.

Now see if you can live a bit of these lives every week!

Huh??

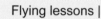 Flying lessons |

Well, for example, have you ever considered taking flying lessons?

Or joining a scuba diving club?

Wow! I'd never thought of that!

A game taken from the excellent book *The Artist's Way* by Julia Cameron.

Activity 7 - Part 2
Five lives exercise

Now think about how you could live a little bit of each one of these lives — what could you do to make this happen?

The multitemporal Bermuda triangle

WARNING!

Your emotional compass is an AWESOME tool!

It has just one TINY WEAK POINT, which is that it can go haywire and become totally inoperable if you find yourself in different time zones at the same time!*

BEEP! BEEP! BEEP!

WHAT'S GOING ON?

WE'RE CROSSING A MULTITEMPORAL FIELD OF TURBULENCE, CAPTAIN! ALL OUR NAVIGATIONAL DEVICES ARE GOING HAYWIRE!

WHEN WE'RE IN THE PRESENT
AND THE PAST/FUTURE AT
ONCE, OUR THOUGHTS CREATE
FAKE EMOTIONS.

I should have said something...

ANGER ABOUT A
FAKE PAST

+

What if I can't do it... ?

FEAR OF A
FAKE FUTURE

=

TURBULENT
EMOTIONS
THAT MUST NOT
BE TRUSTED WHEN
MAKING DECISIONS!

*Thank you, Lulumineuse, for this explanation!

This is why many spiritual traditions suggest doing
ONE THING AT A TIME*, and always coming back to the
PRESENT MOMENT.

WHEN I'M BRUSHING
MY TEETH, I FOCUS ONLY ON
BRUSHING MY TEETH.

And like Mikel
Defays** says,
the simplest way
to come back to
the present is to
become aware of
your BODY.

Really?

YES! BECAUSE
EVEN THOUGH
YOUR MIND
CAN JUMP
BACK AND
FORTH IN
TIME...

I'm a time machine!
Youhouuuu!

Blabla bla"...

BODY: "I CAN'T BE
TELEPORTED EVERY
TWO SECONDS,
BUDDY!"

YOUR BODY ALWAYS STAYS
IN THE PRESENT.

60

To stay in the present, there's lots of fun things you can do WITH YOUR FIVE SENSES! You can:

FEEL: the contact of your clothes, the pattern of your breathing, the sensations in your body, the touch of things...

OBSERVE TINY DETAILS OR SEE THE BIG PICTURE...

SMELL THE AROMAS AROUND YOU...

You can also LISTEN to sounds from the outside and the inside.

Sounds great!

And when you eat, pay attention to all the various FLAVOURS!

*See Eckhart Tolle's *The Power of Now* or Thích Nhất Hạnh's mindfulness.
**life coach, teacher and therapist.

Art-mella

Mindfulness cookies

In theory, "mindfulness" (being completely present in everything we do) seemed so simple I didn't really bother incorporating it into my life. Then, one day...

Nom nom nom...

Crunch! Crunch! Yum!

Oh no! I've plowed through nearly all the cookies and I hardly tasted a single one!

Alright! I'm going to enjoy this next one with all my senses!

Mmm... The scrumptious, sweet smell of chocolate that tickles the tip of my nose and fills my palate...

Wow, it's the first time I've actually noticed this pretty pattern!

And the slightly bumpy texture of the cookie between my fingers...

Yum! The aroma that enters with the first bite, the feel of the chocolate melting on my lips and the dry biscuit on my tongue...

The cookie crunches and mixes with... mmm... the creamy chocolate that glides into the back of my mouth and caresses my palate...

Plus all these sparkles that I can't find words to describe!

Wow! All these sensations in a single cookie!

That was so totally delicious that one was more than enough!

I'll keep the last one for later.

Hey, that reminds me of a film my cousin is in!*

* Ratatouille

63

I started doing the same thing for everything I ate...

Things that I liked...

... and things
I liked a bit less...

(sour thingy)

If I focused on what happened
inside my mouth instead of holding
back or waiting for it to be over,
suddenly the sensation became...

... interesting!?!

Oh! It feels sort of warm up there, tickling my gums, and with all the saliva filling my mouth, and...

I feel like an alien experiencing human life!

Here's a little game to try next time you experience something pleasant or not so pleasant...

"I'm an alien experimenting human emotions!"

Let's see what happens... Whoa! Fascinating!

Art-mella

Activity 8
Using your senses

It's time to be as quiet as a mouse. Set a timer for one minute and just listen.

How many different noises can you hear? Even the really quiet ones — like the creak of a floorboard in another room or a bird on a branch outside the window.

Listen out for far away noises and close ones too, such as the sound of an aeroplane overhead or your breathing.

When the minute is up, see how many things you can recall that you heard and write them down in the big ears on this page!

Activity 9
Positive self-talk

It's amazing how you can change how you feel just by changing your thoughts! The next two activities will show you how to build your positive self-talk skills. Positive self-talk is when we talk kindly to ourselves in a reassuring and helpful way, for example, imagine you didn't do as well as you hoped in a test. It's easy to say to yourself, "Silly me, I should have done better." But a more reassuring and optimistic thing to say to yourself would be, "I did the best I could that day and mistakes are part of learning. I will keep trying and next time I know I will do so much better."

Have a go here. What would be a kind thing to say to yourself if the following happened?

You spill orange juice on your favourite top.

You forget to bring your homework to school.

Activity 10
Positive affirmations

Saying and thinking nice things about yourself will give you a big confidence boost. If you do it every day, it can make you worry less as well as improve your overall health and well-being. Here are some things that you can say to yourself every day:

I can do whatever
I set my mind to

I can make a difference

I believe in me

I love myself

I am awesome

Can you add some positive affirmations of your own?

Neutralizing a thought

BUDDHIST SAGES TEACH US THAT SUFFERING COMES FROM BELIEVING OUR THOUGHTS.

THEY SUGGEST WATCHING THOUGHTS GO BY LIKE CLOUDS... WITHOUT BECOMING ATTACHED TO THEM.

SCREGNEUGNEU! BOUH... RAHHH!! GRRR!! GNIAGNIAGNIA!! PFFF! TSSS!!

I DON'T KNOW ABOUT YOU, BUT FOR ME, THERE ARE SOME THOUGHTS I HAVE A HARD TIME FREEING MYSELF FROM!

HOW ABOUT A LITTLE QUANTUM RECIPE TO CHANGE ALL THAT?

I'LL EXPLAIN THE CONCEPT, THEN I'LL GIVE YOU THE RECIPE!

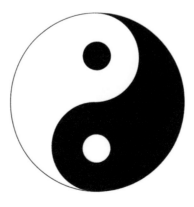

The idea is to be aware that in this world EVERYTHING AND ITS OPPOSITE ARE TRUE AT THE SAME TIME.

This means I am not...

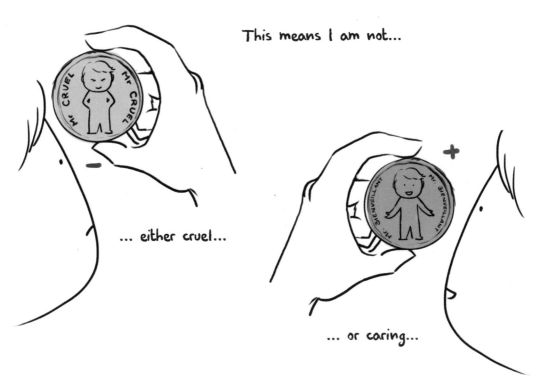

... either cruel...

... or caring...

I have both a cruel and a caring side!

I can see the two sides of reality!

THE SAME IDEA CAN BE APPLIED TO THOUGHTS!

And to neutralize a thought that makes you suffer...

... all you do is balance it with the opposite thought... which is also true!

That's nonsense! How could the opposite of what I think be true?!

Let's give it a try, OK?

Think of a situation that makes you feel bad...

Well, it's about my mother...

When we talk on the phone, it's always about her! She dominates the conversation and it's unbearable!

OK! Write down the thought using this formula: "When... I get the feeling that..."

WHEN ....
.... I GET THE
FEELING THAT ....
....
....

LET'S SEE...
WHEN MY MOTHER TALKS ABOUT HERSELF ENDLESSLY, I GET THE FEELING THAT I MEAN NOTHING TO HER AND THAT I DON'T HAVE A VOICE.

Great! Now try starting the sentence with "It's precisely because..." and say the opposite of your initial thought.

Hm...

"IT'S PRECISELY BECAUSE I MEAN SOMETHING TO HER AND THAT I HAVE A VOICE THAT MY MOTHER TALKS ABOUT HERSELF ENDLESSLY???"*

That makes no sense!!!

Yes, the first time, it's hard to IMAGINE... since we've never had that thought...

... AND THOSE NEURAL CONNECTIONS DON'T EVEN EXIST!

But think about it... Who do you confide in? Someone who you have little respect for?

Um... No.

Generally, it's someone you trust, someone who means something to you, right?

Yes... that's true.

Um...
"I should listen to myself more often. Pay more attention to myself."

Ohhh! It's true, I find it hard to listen to and take care of myself!!

Whoa...

I'm expecting her to do something that I can hardly do myself... !?

Interesting, right?

When you combine the thought that's making you feel bad with its opposite,
BOTH ENERGIES CANCEL EACH OTHER OUT!

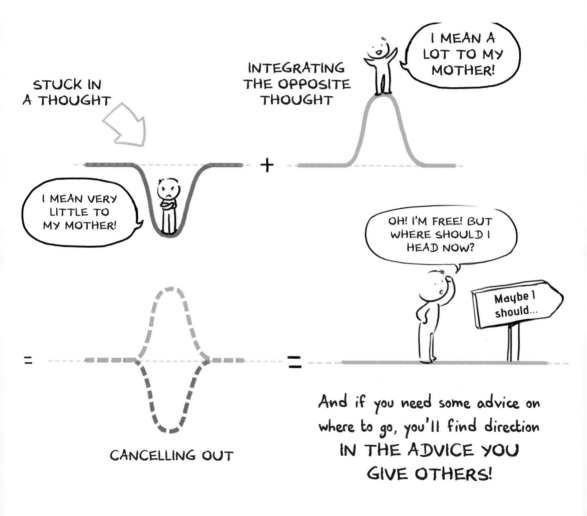

And if you need some advice on
where to go, you'll find direction
**IN THE ADVICE YOU
GIVE OTHERS!**

When a particle and its antiparticle collide, it creates light, and the two energies cancel each other out.

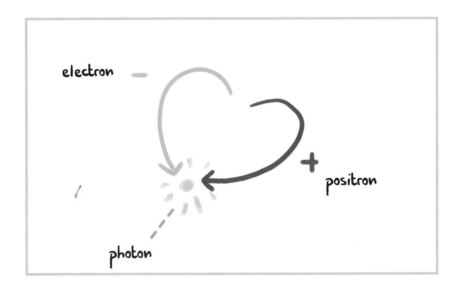

Similarly, when a thought and its opposite collide, it creates a "WOW!" and the two energies CANCEL EACH OTHER OUT...

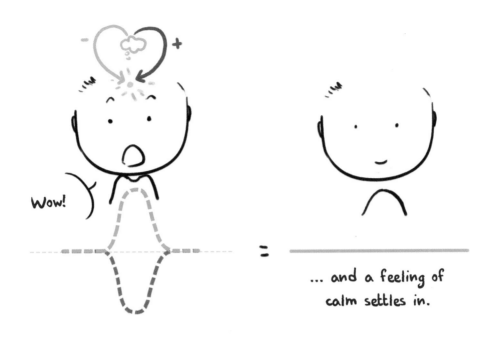

Wow!

... and a feeling of calm settles in.

Inspired by The Work of Byron Katie (www.thework.com).

Activity 11
Turn a negative into a positive

Just like Rattie, you can change your negative thoughts into positive ones.

Have a go yourself on these pages.

When ....

....

....

....

I get the feeling that ....

....

....

....

....

....

....

It's precisely because ....

....

....

that ....

....

....

....

....

What should this person do? ....

....

....

I should ....

....

....

....

Cancelling out a thought

I learned how to love myself unconditionally for the first time thanks to this reversal of thought:

Grr! What a sucker! He should love me unconditionally! Not only when things are going well!

He should be here for me! Besides, I'm not asking for anything special! Just to be here!

I should love myself unconditionally, and not only when things are going well.

I should be here for myself. Not for anything in particular, just to be here.

Ohhh...

That's so true. I like myself when things are going well. And when I feel bad, I want to be someone and someplace else!

I'm asking him to love me unconditionally, yet I don't do so myself...

Right, then. I'll learn!

"I love you.

No matter what.

Go ahead, you can be as sad and lost as you want. I'm here.

I'm here, and I'll always be here for you.

Right here, with you and your pain.

Right here, for as long as you want.

I love you."

Breathe in...

Breathe out...

Art-mella

What radio station are you tuned in to?

By the way, how was the conference you went to, on the connected universe?

Fascinating!!

Nassim Haramein* talked about his latest research on the structure of the universe!

It's funny, at the start of the conference, he said we're like radio stations.

He did?

Yes! And that if we have too many thoughts, it's a sign that we're not tuned in to the right station, that they're just static and it's not normal.

And according to him, the dial that tunes our radio is our emotions! Can you believe it??

Huh?

But how do you turn your emotions dial?

I DON'T KNOW YET, BUT THERE'S GOT TO BE A WAY!

*Physicist who develops theories on "unified fields" and "the connected universe".

Hey!
I did it too!

THAT'S SO COOL! WE FIGURED OUT HOW TO TURN THE DIAL!!

Hey! If we're like radios, maybe the body is like an antenna?

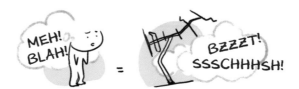

And that's why it's better to keep it in good shape, otherwise it'll pick up too much static!

Nice one... !

BACK WHEN I WAS WORKING ON MY VERY FIRST COMIC BOOK, I WAS VERY NERVOUS.

Time is running out and I'm still stuck!!

THEN, I TOLD MYSELF:

Hey! What if there's a "creativity" station I can connect to so I can be creative whenever I want to??

OK... Remember a moment when I was creative...

And it just flowed out... and my mind felt super clear and full of joy!

Yes! This is what it felt like!!

Scribble, scribble, scribble!

I WAS VERY PROUD TO HAVE FIGURED OUT HOW TO TUNE MY EMOTIONAL DIAL!

LATER, AT AN NLP* WORKSHOP WITH PAUL PYRONNET, I FOUND OUT THAT THE TECHNIQUE ALREADY EXISTED AND HAD EVEN BEEN PERFECTED!

Close your eyes and recall a moment when you felt really good...

Remember the smells, the sensations... Where did you feel it in your body? Can you picture it as a colour? Now, amplify that sensation and colour throughout your entire body, and even beyond!

Keep your eyes closed and take a step back, then imagine that you are leaving this person who feels so good.

*NLP: Neuro-Linguistic Programming.

When you're ready, re-enter this person as you breathe in, and do the gesture you have chosen.

CHOSEN GESTURE

(TO BE REPEATED TEN TO THIRTY TIMES!)

And once again, feel all those feelings of well-being, but now even stronger.

... and the emotions were pre-programmed as "favourite station" buttons on your radio.

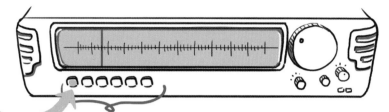

FAVOURITE STATIONS

So it's as if some situations are pushing your buttons and taking you right back to these stations from the past.

Oh! Maybe that's why it feels like I'm always re-living the same situations!

The good news is that we can de-programme or re-programme our favourites!

Whoa! How do you do that??

WELL, THE LITTLE GIRL YOU WERE AT THE TIME WAS STILL FRAGILE.

AND SINCE THE EMOTION, WHICH WAS TOO STRONG, COULD HAVE DAMAGED YOUR CIRCUITS, YOUR PREFRONTAL BRAIN BLEW A FUSE TO PROTECT YOU.

OK, access granted!

Yeah!

NOW THAT YOU'RE OLDER AND YOUR BODY IS STRONG ENOUGH TO HANDLE IT, YOU ARE MORE THAN CAPABLE OF WELCOMING THE EMOTION.

The emotion wasn't able to be experienced fully.

AND THAT'S WHY IT'S KNOCKING!

Finally!! I've been knocking for so long!!!

IT MAY BE A BIT MORE INTENSE, BUT IF YOU WELCOME IT FULLY THEN IT'LL BE DONE!

Thanks! Bye!

THE EMOTION LEAVES AND NEVER COMES BACK!

THE BUTTON IS DE-PROGRAMMED!

Inspired by Luc Geiger's NERTI method (Rapid Emotional Clearing of Subconscious Trauma).

.... then imagine what you would like to experience in the future, and feel all the emotions that come with it, as if it has already happened!

Yeah, I've heard about that, it's like the "law of attraction". But frankly, it's weird... I really don't get how it works!

Do you play a musical instrument?

Uh... yes, I play the violin. Why?

Do you know the difference between an average musician and someone who truly moves the audience?

Talent?

EMOTION!

A great musician incarnates the piece they are playing... They feel it wholeheartedly!

They feel the emotion even
before they start playing!

And when they play, they
render the emotion audible to others...

BUT THE EMOTION WAS THERE ALREADY...
IN THE SILENCE... BEFORE THEY EVEN PLAYED THE FIRST NOTE.

Oh... It's true, I also
feel the emotion before
I play, then I transfer
it to my music.

And you feel it's the
emotion guiding you
when you play, right?

Yes! That's it!

Well, in life it's the same thing: the emotion you feel BEFORE doing anything is what guides your actions and allows you to become the person you would like to be.

You can choose to live your life like an average performer,

or

make your life a WORK OF ART, live it like a maestro, by feeling the emotions that you would like to experience before acting!

Art-mella

Inspired by a conversation with Yves Rossi, a great flight attendant and medium!

Activity 12
Finding joy

When you're feeling down, you can help yourself feel good again by thinking about a happy moment in your life. Draw it here, if you can, and try to add as much detail as you can remember.

What did you see?

What did you hear?

What did you smell?

What did you taste?

What did you feel?

Mmm! That feels so much better!

Seeing the world in panorama

Do you know that the way you look at the world influences your emotions literally? For a while, I'd been memorizing surroundings so I could draw them from memory.

Then one day...

Oh dear! I'm really rushing!

What if I tried doing what I do when I memorize my surroundings?

MULTISENSORY PHOTOGRAPHIC MODE ACTIVATED!

This won't do at all! I can't see anything!

What if I framed it a bit better?

That's better!

Oh... I feel so much calmer suddenly!

That's when I remembered
a friend once telling me:

"Among the exercices that
were given to me to help
me cope with depression,
there was exercising my
peripheral vision."

IN FACT, IT'S SO POWERFUL THAT WE CAN CONDITION
OURSELVES TO LOVE SOMETHING (OR NOT) BY CHANGING
THE MENTAL IMAGE WE HAVE OF IT!

(Inspired by a self-hypnosis workshop with Sobhi Levi)

Shall we do the exercise together?
What do you not like that you wish
you could enjoy more?

Doing my accounting!

OK! Close your
eyes and think of
a moment that you
remember being
very pleasant.

Where is the image?

It takes up the whole space.

- Is the image dark or light?
- Is it blurry or clear?
- Are the colours vivid or are they black and white?
- Are there any smells, sounds or textures?
- Do you see yourself or are you inside the picture?

DETAILS FROM A REALLY PLEASANT MEMORY

- PANORAMIC picture.
- Lots of LIGHT.
- CLEAR.
- Very VIVID COLOURS.
- The SMELL of sea salt, the SOUND of waves, the FEEL of the sand beneath me.
- I can't see myself; I'M IN IT.

Now, think about when you're doing your accounting.

Where do you picture it and what is it like?

It's very small, and at the bottom left. It's dark and blurry.

Ready? We're going to apply the features of your pleasant memory to it!

(Ha! ha! No wonder you don't like doing your accounting!)

Take the image and make it PANORAMIC.

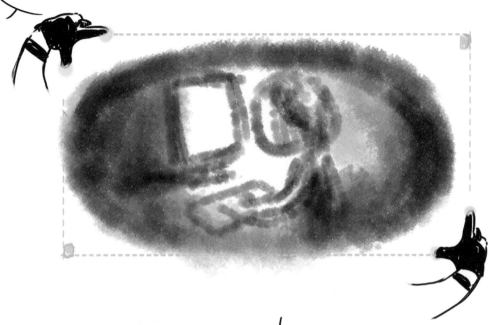

Got it: panoramic image!

Give it some LIGHT!

See all the details very CLEARLY!

Light: check!

Details: check!

Sense the SMELLS and TEXTURES that you love.

Adding the scent of a cup of tea and the feel of a breeze through the window...

Do you like this picture?
Do you want to enter it?

Yes, I do!
Here I go!

THE FINAL RESULT:

So? Do you feel like doing your accounting now?

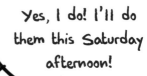

Yes, I do! I'll do them this Saturday afternoon!

I'm also going to put a plant on my desk!

BEFORE RETOUCHING

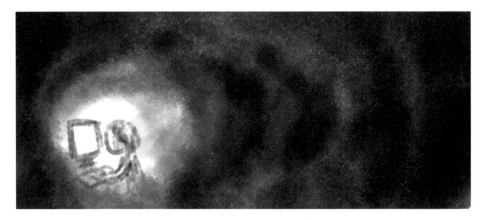

Desire thermometer: 2/10

AFTER RETOUCHING

Desire thermometer: 8/10

What do you think?

Neat, isn't it?

We can also condition ourselves to HATE SOMETHING or RETOUCH A PAINFUL MEMORY to make it neutral.

PERSONALLY, I DECIDED TO TAKE SOME NICE PHOTOS RIGHT AWAY...
TO AVOID HAVING TO RETOUCH THEM LATER!

Oh...
this photo is
a bit sad!

No wonder
I've got the
blues!

That's better!

Besides, if life is a journey,
we might as well take some
nice pictures along the way,
don't you think?

Art-mella

Activity 13
Changing your view

Draw a panorama of where you are sitting right now. Make it bursting with colour — brighter than real life!

Finding words

TO ENRICH THE WAY I EXPRESS MY EMOTIONS, I ONCE
TRIED HANGING A VOCABULARY LIST IN THE BATHROOM...

Moved

Inspired

Overwhelmed

Euphoric

Jubilant

Joyous

Vexed

Restored

BUT AFTER TWO YEARS, WHEN SOMEBODY ASKED ME:

How are you doing?

I'D STILL JUST ANSWER:

Good.

OR

Alright.

But then, I discovered that emotions can be described as opening or closing, and outward-facing or inward-facing:

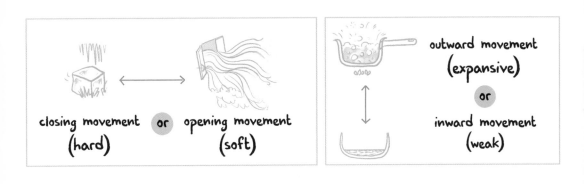

closing movement
(hard)   **or**   opening movement
(soft)

outward movement
(expansive)
or
inward movement
(weak)

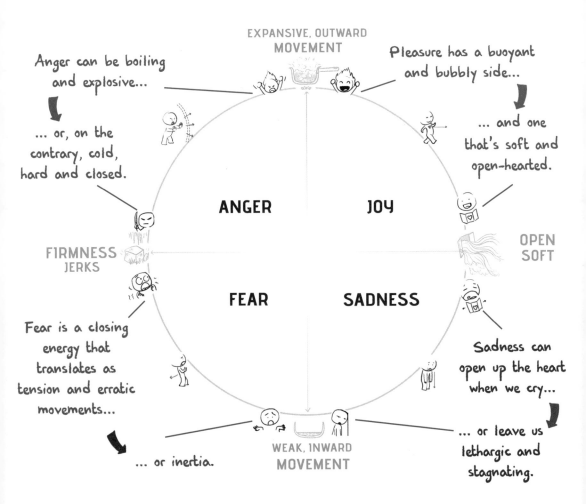

EXPANSIVE, OUTWARD
MOVEMENT

Anger can be boiling and explosive...

Pleasure has a buoyant and bubbly side...

... or, on the contrary, cold, hard and closed.

... and one that's soft and open-hearted.

ANGER   **JOY**

FIRMNESS
JERKS

OPEN
SOFT

FEAR   **SADNESS**

Fear is a closing energy that translates as tension and erratic movements...

Sadness can open up the heart when we cry...

... or inertia.

WEAK, INWARD
MOVEMENT

... or leave us lethargic and stagnating.

INSPIRED BY A CONFERENCE BY ADRIEN PIRET.

Hm... interesting.

But how is this useful?

Aha! Well, it helped me to find the words to express my emotions more easily...

WORDS

Now, I can find the word that describes what I'm feeling in a cinch!

Activity 14
Emotions chart

Here's your emotions chart — you can look at this page whenever you need to find the word (or words) to express how you are feeling.

You can add some words of your own too!

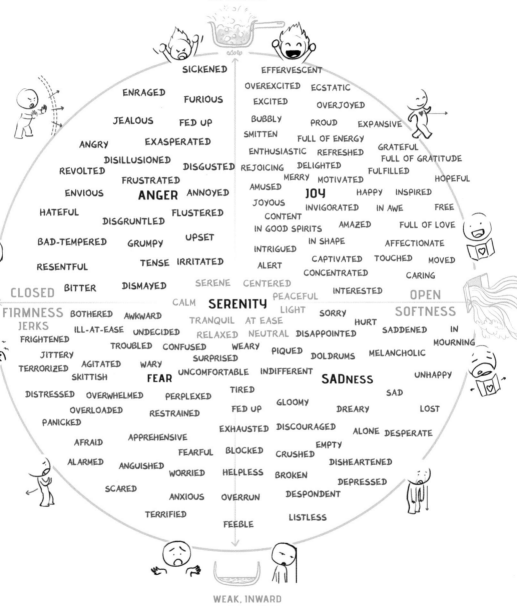

EXPANSIVE, OUTWARD
MOVEMENT

SICKENED   EFFERVESCENT
ENRAGED   FURIOUS   OVEREXCITED   ECSTATIC
                      EXCITED   OVERJOYED
JEALOUS   FED UP   BUBBLY   PROUD   EXPANSIVE
ANGRY   EXASPERATED   SMITTEN   FULL OF ENERGY
DISILLUSIONED   ENTHUSIASTIC   REFRESHED   GRATEFUL
REVOLTED   DISGUSTED   REJOICING   DELIGHTED   FULL OF GRATITUDE
FRUSTRATED   MERRY   MOTIVATED   FULFILLED   HOPEFUL
ENVIOUS   **ANGER**   ANNOYED   AMUSED   **JOY**   HAPPY   INSPIRED
HATEFUL   FLUSTERED   JOYOUS   INVIGORATED   IN AWE   FREE
DISGRUNTLED   CONTENT   AMAZED   FULL OF LOVE
BAD-TEMPERED   GRUMPY   UPSET   IN GOOD SPIRITS   IN SHAPE   AFFECTIONATE
RESENTFUL   TENSE   IRRITATED   INTRIGUED   CAPTIVATED   TOUCHED   MOVED
                      ALERT   CONCENTRATED   CARING
BITTER   DISMAYED   SERENE   CENTERED   INTERESTED
CLOSED   CALM   **SERENITY**   PEACEFUL   OPEN
FIRMNESS   BOTHERED   AWKWARD   LIGHT   SORRY   SOFTNESS
JERKS   ILL-AT-EASE   UNDECIDED   TRANQUIL   AT EASE   HURT   SADDENED   IN
FRIGHTENED   TROUBLED   CONFUSED   RELAXED   NEUTRAL   DISAPPOINTED   MOURNING
JITTERY   SURPRISED   WEARY   PIQUED   DOLDRUMS   MELANCHOLIC
TERRORIZED   AGITATED   WARY   UNCOMFORTABLE   INDIFFERENT   UNHAPPY
SKITTISH   **FEAR**   TIRED   **SADness**   SAD
DISTRESSED   OVERWHELMED   PERPLEXED   GLOOMY   LOST
OVERLOADED   RESTRAINED   FED UP   DREARY
PANICKED   EXHAUSTED   DISCOURAGED   ALONE   DESPERATE
AFRAID   APPREHENSIVE   EMPTY
ALARMED   FEARFUL   BLOCKED   CRUSHED   DISHEARTENED
ANGUISHED   WORRIED   HELPLESS   BROKEN   DEPRESSED
SCARED   OVERRUN   DESPONDENT
ANXIOUS   LISTLESS
TERRIFIED   FEEBLE

WEAK, INWARD
MOVEMENT

Finding the message behind the emotion

Oh dear! That must have been upsetting to see your friends turn away when you were trying to tell them what was going on inside you.

It was! Now what do I do to express my emotions??

If you'd like, to get out of this rut, we can try to find the hidden need behind your emotions. You up for it?

How do we do that?

Art-mella

LET'S INVESTIGATE, SHALL WE?!

(TO BE CONTINUED IN VOLUME 2!)

Glossary

Acupuncture – A traditional form of Chinese medicine that involves inserting thin needles into specific points on the body to stimulate and balance the flow of energy. You can also experience the benefits of acupuncture by tapping acupressure points, like Art-mella and Rattie do on page 19!

Bermuda Triangle – A place in the Atlantic Ocean – near Florida, Puerto Rico and Bermuda – where some people believe that planes and ships have disappeared in mysterious ways. No one knows for sure why these things happen, and scientists are still trying to figure it out!

Conditioning – The process of changing your thoughts or behaviour through repetition and association. For example, Art-mella feels better about her accounting when she's trained her mind to associate it with a positive mental image.

Herbicide – A chemical that's used to kill unwanted plants or weeds.

Multitemporal – Something that involves multiple points in time.

NERTI Technique – NERTI stands for "Non-Emotional Rehearsal Technique and Integration". It involves practising a calm response to a stressful situation, so that the response becomes automatic when the situation arises.

Neural Connections – Pathways that allow different parts of the brain to communicate with each other.

Neuro-linguistic Programming (NLP) – This method studies how people use language to create their own experiences, and it's used to help people improve their communication.

Nonviolent Communication (NVC) – A way of communicating that emphasizes empathy and understanding.

Pranayama – A type of yoga that involves controlling the breath to promote relaxation, focus and well-being.

Prefontal Brain – Officially known as the prefontal cortex, this part of your brain is located behind your forehead. It's responsible for many things, including decision-making, problem-solving and regulating emotions.

Psychological Boundaries – Invisible lines that help us feel safe and respected in our relationships with others. Just like we have rules at home and school to keep us safe, we also have rules for how we want others to treat us.

Quantum Healing – An approach to well-being that believes the mind and body are connected. It suggests that changing your thoughts and emotions can have a positive effect on your physical health.

Qigong – A type of exercise and meditation that involves slow, gentle movements, deep breathing and mindfulness.

Sage – A wise person who is respected for their knowledge and experience.

The Subconscious – The part of your mind that holds thoughts and feelings that you're not fully aware of. These thoughts and feelings can influence your behaviour and emotions, even though you may not be conscious of them.

TIPI Method – A method that involves tuning in to physical sensations in your body to help you release your emotions.

Unconditionally – When you love yourself unconditionally it means that no matter what you do or what happens, you will always accept and appreciate yourself exactly as you are.

About the Author

Armella Leung was born in Madagascar. At the age of 17, she travelled to France to study graphic design, motion design, arts and new technologies.

She threw herself into her studies with passion and gave them her all – but the beginning of her working life was a shock. What? Was that how her life was going to look? Spending eight hours a day in a dark room in front of a computer? Participating in pollution and feeling like a destructive virus on the planet? Impossible!

It was the beginning of a search for meaning that lead her to study permaculture and to begin the practice of meditation, Tai chi, qigong and martial arts. From her exploration of consciousness, the mind-and-body connection and the laws of nature arose the desire to transmit all this knowledge that felt so fundamental to her – knowledge that she was surprised not to have learned before.

Armella started a comic blog in 2013 to begin sharing her discoveries in a light and playful way. In 2014, she worked as a graphic designer in the world of education and scientific research... because changing the world begins with education, right?

But stormy relationships during this time forced her to realize that all the violence she thought was outside of her was also inside of her – and that she did not have communication skills at all!

She then discovered NVC – Nonviolent Communication – which seemed to her like the missing link between her ideals of goodwill and the means to actually take care of oneself and one's relationships. And, rather than changing the world, she decided to change her own life first! From then, making her dreams come true would be her full-time job!

Well... what she actually discovered were all the fears and blockages there were between her and her dreams... But if she had one resource, it was the belief that anything can be learned!

If she lacked entrepreneurial skills, she would enrol on a course! If emotions were a hindrance, she would get training in emotional freeing techniques. Self-sabotage starting to show its teeth? She would learn self-hypnosis techniques. Every problem would find its solution…

And it worked! Her life began to look like her dreams. She met interesting people and discovered exciting ideas: sometimes scientific ideas, sometimes spiritual, therapeutic or quantum ideas. Then a publisher contacted her to publish her comics strips.

Her first book, *Friandises philosophiques* (*Philosophical Treats*), was published by Pourpenser Editions in 2015, and a strong desire to share all the emotional tools that changed her life arose. How come she didn't learn all these tools at school?

Well, that's how this book came to be!

The Emotions Chart

Head to Art-mella's website to find a free printable version of the emotions chart!

www.art-mella.com/site/emotions1/

Notes

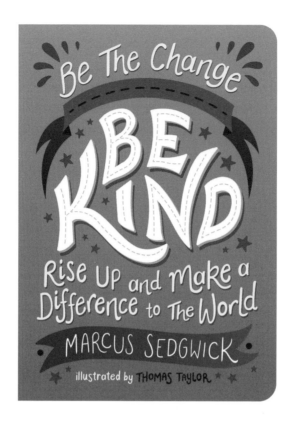

Be The Change – Be Kind

Rise Up and Make a Difference to the World

Marcus Sedgwick

Paperback

978-1-80007-411-8

Kindness is cool! It can create positive change in all our lives. *Be The Change: Be Kind* is your handbook on how to use your own voice to empower yourself and others to spread kindness. Award-winning author Marcus Sedgwick tells the story of kindness – where it comes from, what it feels like and perhaps most importantly why it matters.

Be The Change – Be Calm

Rise Up and Don't Let Anxiety Hold You Back

Marcus Sedgwick

Paperback

978-1-80007-412-5

Be The Change: Be Calm will show you how to shut down anxiety with fun and simple ways to calm your mind by listening to what your body is telling you. Ever tried the half-salamander exercise? And have you ever performed a body scan? These amazing activities along with many others will become your toolkit to a calmer and happier life.

This is Me!

A Self-Discovery Journal for Girls

Paperback

978-1-80007-165-0

Welcome to the time in your life when lots of exciting stuff happens! This companion is here to guide you along the way. It's full of fabulous fill-in activities, helping you plan and prepare for big days, like starting a new school, and offering some great ideas when you need a happiness boost – covering the essentials and so much more!

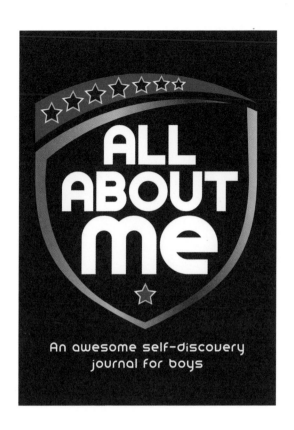

All About Me

An Awesome Self-Discovery Journal for Boys

Paperback

978-1-80007-554-2

Welcome to the time in your life when lots of big, exciting stuff happens! This companion is here to guide you along the way. It's full of cool fill-in activities, helping you plan and prepare for big days, like starting a new school, and offering some great ideas when you need a confidence boost – covering the essentials and so much more!

Have you enjoyed this book? If so, find us on Facebook
at Summersdale Publishers, on Twitter at @Summersdale
and on Instagram and TikTok at @summersdalebooks
and get in touch. We'd love to hear from you!

www.summersdale.com